CELEBRATE THANKSGIVING

by Elvie L. Butler

illustrated by William Van Horn

SCHOLASTIC INC.
New York   Toronto   London   Auckland   Sydney

For my parents,
to whom I owe
a thousand thank yous.

ISBN 0-590-42505-6

Copyright © 1989 by Elvie L. Butler.
Illustrations © 1989 by Scholastic Inc.
All rights reserved. Published by Scholastic Inc.

12 11 10 9 8 7 6 5 4 3 2 1   8 9/8 0 1 2 3 3/9

Printed in the U.S.A.   33

First Scholastic printing, October 1989

How to Celebrate Thanksgiving

This book has **cartoon pages, activity pages,** and **stickers.**

The **cartoon pages** tell a story about the Greenfield Gang's Thanksgiving celebration. After each page of the story, there is **an activity page** that's fun to fill out.

* To answer the True, False, or Maybe questions, use the turkey stickers from the sticker pages.

* For the multiple choice questions, put a check in front of the answer you like. Here's the good news — there are no wrong answers! The answer you give will be the right answer for your book. (You may choose as many answers as you like!)

* On some activity pages, there are blank squares marked "Sticker." You will find a sticker that belongs in the square on the sticker sheets.

* You can also color and decorate the answer pages any way you like.

Introducing the characters who will help you celebrate Thanksgiving

The 2-W Weasels

Walter and Willa, the 2-W Weasels, live in a walnut tree in the Big Green Field. They like to get together with all their friends to celebrate any and every event of the year.

The Kittens and Puppies

These lively little animals love to chase each other around the Big Green Field, and sometimes they end up fighting.

Group Leader Gooper and the Owl Goopers

The Owl Goopers are a team of very smart owls whose job it is to find out what things are about. Under the direction of Group Leader Gooper they gather information to program into the mini-computers that fit in their backpacks.

Maestro Gabriel Groundhog with his Choir and Band

Every year on February 2nd, Gabriel Groundhog comes out of his burrow after a long winter's sleep. If he sees his shadow, he goes back in. If he does not see it, then he stays out and conducts his choir of birds and his band.

All these friends together are called
"The Greenfield Gang."

and now . . .
You Are Invited to Join
THE GREENFIELD GANG
because . . .

IT'S THANKSGIVING TIME!

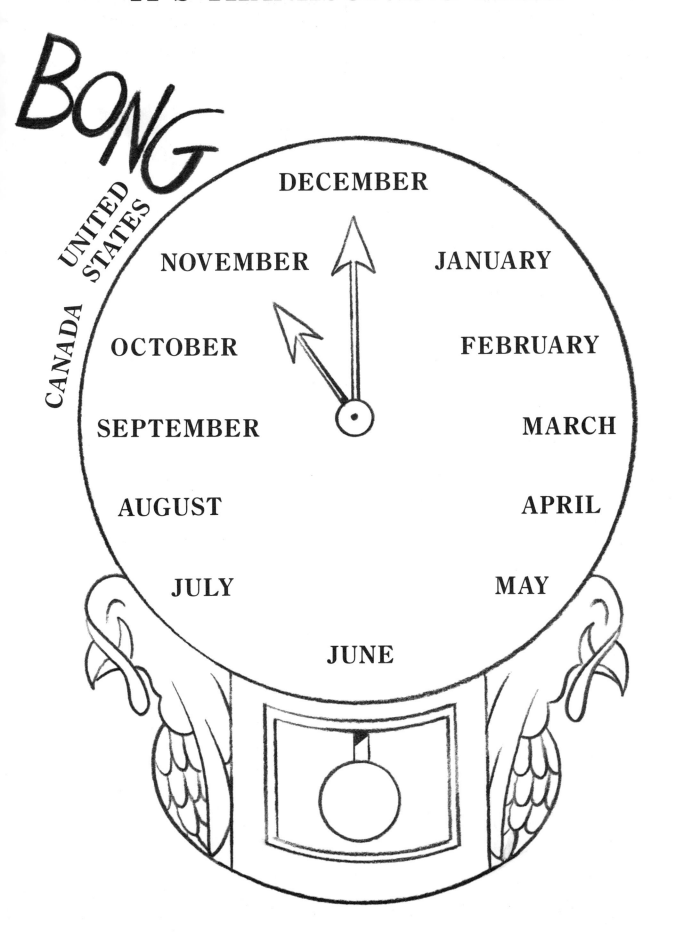

BONG

CANADA   UNITED STATES

DECEMBER

NOVEMBER   JANUARY

OCTOBER   FEBRUARY

SEPTEMBER   MARCH

AUGUST   APRIL

JULY   MAY

JUNE

The Kittens and Puppies were playing in the Big Green Field, and the 2-W Weasels were busy in the walnut tree, making plans for Thanksgiving.

I'll put bright autumn leaves between the ribbons and bows. Oh, Walter! This will be a wonderful hat!

I'm sure it will. Let's roast a stuffed pumpkin for Thanksgiving, like we did last year — remember? We ate around a campfire.

That was fun. We'll roast corn and potatoes, too, and marshmallows for dessert. I can hardly wait! Walter, are you listening?

I was thinking about the campfire. Last year one of the Puppies burned his paw. We should —

Is someone knocking at the tree?

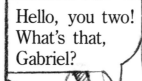

Hello, you two! What's that, Gabriel?

It's our list of suggestions for Thanksgiving. What's wrong, Walter?

It's about the Thanksgiving campfire. We must be sure nobody gets hurt this year.

I'll be Vice-President-in-charge-of-the-Campfire. Everything will be just fine.

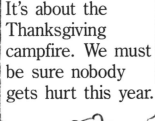

I hope we can have a few colors of Jell-O for Thanksgiving — it's so lovely.

Of course. And it's time for tea and Jell-O right now.

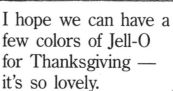

1. These are some of my Thanksgiving plans:

_____ rake leaves

_____ send dinner invitations

_____ make a wonderful hat

_____ clean my room

_____ bake a pie 2 inches high

and _____

or _____

and also _____

4. Please draw and color your Thanksgiving hat.

MY PERSONAL
THANKSGIVING HAT

2. When I make Thanksgiving dinner, I

will have _____ pumpkin pie _____ hot dogs

_____ candy salad _____ mashed potatoes

_____ veggie burgers _____ refried beans

_____ roast turkey _____ peanut butter

_____ broccoli _____ tofu _____ pirogies

and _____

and also _____

Sticker

Willa's hat

3. Every campfire should have at least one adult Vice-President in charge of it.

_____ Yes or _____ No, because _____

_____

Sticker

Firehat

1. True or False or Maybe

There are many different kinds of sanctuaries.

Turkey gobbling noises sound very musical.

The Kittens and Puppies could hurt the turkeys.

If the turkeys get in a fight with the Kittens and Puppies, the turkeys will win.

Sticker

A turkey feather

2. Dear Me,

When Willa Weasel sees

the Turkey Sanctuary,

she will _____

_____

_____

_____

Yours truly,

Me

3. When I build a sanctuary, it will be for:

_____ birds

_____ dogs

_____ spiders

_____ gerbils

_____ goldfish

_____ children

_____ teachers

_____ frogs

or _____

4. Would you please finish and color your sanctuary sign.

9

1. When the Kittens and Puppies patrol the turkeys, it will be:

_____ loud and busy   _____ very well done

_____ quiet and peaceful   _____ a dismal affair

_____ dangerous   or _____

2. If I need to find my own food, I

look for _____ a vegetable garden

_____ wild berries _____ a cookie jar

_____ a honeycomb _____ a Jell-O tree

_____ a potato chip bush _____ peas

or _____

Sticker

A cookie jar

Sticker

A mini-computer

3. Turkeys are:

_____ totally beautiful

_____ somewhat lovely

_____ fairly attractive

_____ ordinary-looking

_____ a little clumsy

_____ not too pretty

_____ a bit unlovely

_____ quite ugly

_____ scary-looking

and _____

and also _____

Please color
the turkey.
(It's a boy)

The Owl Goopers Wish to Announce That Turkeys Used To Be Dinosaurs, Maybe

While searching for clues to turkey history, the Owl Goopers read in the Greenfield Gazette that turkeys may have evolved from dinosaurs.

This clue came from a scientist who thinks dinosaurs changed a tiny bit every day for bezillions of years. (That is called evolving.) They changed and changed and got smaller and smaller until they were more like turkeys than dinosaurs. However, they still have three-toed scaly feet like Tyrannosaurus Rex had, and they have mini-dinosaur tailbones.

The Owl Goopers feel it is lucky that dinosaurs changed to turkeys, because a dinosaur would not fit into a roasting pan, and a dinosaur platter would break the table.

The Goopers then discovered that Benjamin Franklin wanted to make the turkey America's national bird. The Owls feel that owls should have been the national bird, and suspect that turkeys feel as rejected as they do.

Then the Goopers read about a turkey gnat (black fly), a turkey fish (lion fish), and also about a bouncy, old-fashioned American dance called the turkey trot. They wonder if this dance is done by turkeys, or by Americans.

The Owl Goopers then found clues to other kinds of turkeys, such as Australian ones called bustards and turkey vultures called buzzards. The Goopers suggest that you do not tell the 2-W Weasels about the bustard and buzzard, as they might think these are lovely names for twins, which they are not.

The Owl Goopers Wish to Thank You For Your Attention

1. True or False or Maybe

Australian people probably eat bustard and mustard hotdogs, and bustard burgers.

If evolution were to go backwards, then turkeys would change back into dinosaurs.

A bezillion is ten times more than the biggest number in the universe.

Chickens also have three-toed scaly feet, and so do South American tree sloths.

If the national bird were a turkey, we would have roast eagle for Thanksgiving dinner.

On Thanksgiving day, all turkeys dance the turkey trot, and go fishing for turkey fish.

2. If turkeys start to change back into dinosaurs, they might look like this:

3. . . . and then they might look like this:

After 500 years of backward evolution.

After 5000 years of backward evolution.

1. For trying to do a good job, the Kittens and Puppies get an _____A _____B _____C+ _____C _____C− or _____

Comments: _____

_____

A Patrol Kitten

2. After 50,000 years of backward evolution, a turkey might look like this:

A Patrol Puppy

A scared turkey

3. True or False or Maybe

When the Kittens and Puppies chase and fight, they are being normal and having fun.

When you must do something boring, you will not be bored if you make up stories and songs while you're doing it.

15

The Owl Goopers Wish to Announce That Thanksgiving Has a History

While searching for clues to Thanksgiving, the Owl Goopers discovered that it started when people came from the eastern side of the Atlantic Ocean to make a better life for themselves on the western side. They came in 1620 in a ship called the Mayflower, and they landed near a place called Plymouth Rock.

First they were called the Old Comers, but they weren't really old, so then they were called the Forefathers, and that was quite good. Two hundred years later Daniel Webster called them Pilgrims, and soon they were known as Pilgrim Fathers. The Goopers are sure Mr. Webster meant Pilgrim Mothers as well as Fathers, and would have said that if he had thought of it.

The Pilgrim Mothers and Fathers had a hard time on the western side. There were no houses to buy, no freeways to travel, and no supermarkets. They had to make everything. Finally, they were able to clear enough ground to plant food, and Indians showed them how to grow corn. When they had a harvest, they were so thankful that they took a day off to have a feast and give thanks to God. They invited the Indians, too — one hundred came!

The Pilgrims did not have a feast every year, though, since Thanksgiving was not actually a holiday. Finally, in 1863, a nice lady called Sarah Hale asked President Abraham Lincoln to make Thanksgiving an Official Holiday, and so he did.

The Owl Goopers Wish to Thank You for Your Attention

1. True or False or Maybe

The Pilgrim Fathers and Mothers actually landed at Provincetown before they found Plymouth Rock.

The Pilgrims were called "Old Comers" because they came from the Old World.

Daniel Webster was a statesman and public speaker, and he also wrote a dictionary.

2. People came across the ocean to the western side because they were:

_____ on a treasure hunt.

_____ not free to worship their own way.

_____ on the wrong ship.

or _____

3. Dear Me,

If I decide to look for a new

place where I can make a better life

for myself, I will _____

_____

_____

_____

_____

Respectfully yours,

Me

Sticker

Pilgrim Father

Sticker

Pilgrim Mother

Sticker

The Mayflower

Sticker

Indian Guest

17

One night the Kittens and Puppies were so frustrated from patrolling all day that they could not get to sleep, so Walter made up a bedtime story for them.

Once upon a time, my ancestors, the Greyrock Gang, lived at a place near Plymouth Rock.

One day the Greyrock Gang looked out over the ocean and saw something big, and the closer it got, the bigger it got.

It was a ship. It landed on their beach, and some Pilgrims got off and walked onto the land.

One of the Pilgrims said to the Greyrock Gang, "How do you do? My name is Miles Standish. We hope to make a better life in this new land. The first thing we need is food."

Another Pilgrim stepped forward and said, "We want to be friends, but we are starved, and you look tasty!" The Greyrock Gang was terrified, but my brave great-great-great-great-grandfather spoke up.

"I'm very sorry," he said, "but we are tough and bitter. The Indians never eat us — they prefer corn. They will give you

some and show you how to make corn fritters."

And so the Pilgrims ate corn fritters and lived peacefully beside the Greyrock Gang.

1. Walter Weasel's bedtime story is:

_____ Excellent _____ Very good _____ Good _____ Average _____ Fair

because _____

2. This is my short bedtime story for the Kittens and Puppies.

MY ANCESTORS

_____

_____

_____

_____

_____

CONTINUED on page 44

Sticker

A Sleeping Puppy

Sticker

A Sleeping Kitten

Number
of stories
I have written
_____

Please color the turkey.
(It's a girl)

MAESTRO GROUNDHOG'S OAK TREE

Please color the picture, and paste the leaves back on the tree.
The leaf stickers are at the back of the book.

The Greenfield Gang was making Official Certificates of Thanksgiving, and the Kittens and Puppies were on patrol at the Turkey Sanctuary.

Is it true, G.L. that, um, Canadian Thanksgiving is in October, and American Thanksgiving is in November?

Yes, it's true. Canada celebrates Thanksgiving on the second Monday of October, and the United States on the fourth Thursday of November.

That must be because Canada is farther north. The weather turns colder sooner, so harvest is sooner.

I believe that is right.

What's that racket?

Sounds like trouble at the Turkey Sanctuary!

The Kittens and Puppies are gone!

Oh, no!

Maybe they're hiding. We must search everywhere!

Oh, Walter, I'm afraid they've run away! This is awful.

They were too young for such hard duty.

1. Would you please write
this news report.

```
┌─────────────────────────────────┐
│                                 │
│   THE GREENFIELD GAZETTE        │
│                                 │
│     * * * * * * *               │
│                                 │
│   KITTENS AND PUPPIES           │
│        MISSING                  │
│                                 │
│   Today in the Big Green Field, │
│                                 │
│   _____ │
│                                 │
│   _____ │
│                                 │
│   _____ │
│                                 │
│   _____ │
│                                 │
│   _____ │
│                                 │
└─────────────────────────────────┘
```

2. Dear Me,

I am worried about the Kittens
and Puppies because

_____

_____

_____

_____

Sincerely yours,

Me

_____

My signature

3. The best way to solve a problem is to:

_____ ask for help   _____ run away

_____ hide in a closet   _____ yell and shout

_____ think it over   or _____

```
┌ ─ ─ ─ ─ ─ ┐     ┌ ─ ─ ─ ─ ─ ┐     ┌ ─ ─ ─ ─ ─ ┐
│           │     │           │     │           │
│  Sticker  │     │  Sticker  │     │  Sticker  │
│           │     │           │     │           │
└ ─ ─ ─ ─ ─ ┘     └ ─ ─ ─ ─ ─ ┘     └ ─ ─ ─ ─ ─ ┘
   Harvest          Canadian          American
  vegetables      Thanksgiving      Thanksgiving
```

Please complete and decorate this Certificate.

OFFICIAL CERTIFICATE OF THANKSGIVING

BE IT HEREBY KNOWN THAT I, _____

Name

of _____

Address

DO SOLEMNLY STATE THAT I am thankful for, and will henceforth continue to be thankful for, the following:

BE IT FURTHER KNOWN THAT I shall also, at all times, be thankful for all such goods and services as shall be received by me throughout the year, AND THAT WHEREAS such goods and services become my own, they shall at all times be shared with those I love.

Completed at _____ on the _____ day of _____,
in the year one thousand nine hundred and _____.

_____

Signature

SIGNED, SEALED AND DELIVERED by

_____

please print

in the presence of:

Affix Official

Seal in this

space. →

Seal of

Thanksgiving

Sticker

_____

Signature of Witness

Please complete and decorate these Thank You Checklists.

THANK YOU CHECKLIST FOR CHILDREN

_____ food and shelter

_____ friends and fun

_____ homework and chores

_____ clothing and toys

_____ sunny days

_____ green vegetables

_____ aunts and uncles

and _____

and also _____

THANK YOU CHECKLIST FOR GRANDPARENTS

_____ grandchildren

_____ friends and fun

_____ love and laughter

_____ teeth

_____ comfortable shoes

_____ naughty children

_____ flowers and plants

_____ good health

and _____

THANK YOU CHECKLIST FOR PARENTS

_____ children

_____ food and shelter

_____ good jobs

_____ weekends and holidays

_____ friends and family

_____ lazy children

_____ taxes

_____ clothes and shoes

and _____

THANK YOU CHECKLIST FOR TEACHERS

_____ recess and noon hour

_____ good pupils

_____ noisy classes

_____ tasty lunches

_____ good principals

_____ torn books

_____ good friends

_____ summer holidays

and _____

GREENFIELD GAZETTE NEWS BULLETIN!
Kittens and Puppies Still Missing. Big Search Underway.

1. Six colors of Jell-O would be:

_____ cherry

_____ blueberry

_____ cabbage

_____ rutabaga

_____ lemon

_____ watermelon

_____ orange

_____ soya bean

_____ kiwi fruit

_____ purple grape

_____ gooseberry

_____ lime

or _____

Sticker

A lost Kitten

Sticker

A lost Puppy

2. Dear Me,

If I ever have to put up a Reward,

I will offer _____

_____

_____

Very truly yours,

Me

3. Would you please draw and color the Reward Poster.

GREENFIELD GAZETTE NEWS BULLETIN!

Owl Goopers Ready to Crack Case of Mysterious Disappearance

1. The Greenfield Gang should:

_____ return the turkeys immediately.

_____ try another rescue attempt.

_____ wait for the Kittens and Puppies to escape by themselves.

or _____

GREENFIELD GAZETTE NEWS BULLETIN!

Kittens and Puppies in great danger. Rescue attempt fails!

2. True or False or Maybe

It is all right for the Greenfield Gang to be out on a cold dark night.

It is dangerous for small children to be out alone on a cold dark night.

The Kittens and Puppies are happy at the turkey farm and do not want to come home.

The turkey farmer is acting brave, but is really afraid of the Greenfield Gang.

3. For bravely demanding to see the

Kittens and Puppies, Walter gets

an _____ A _____ B _____ C+ _____ C

_____ C− _____ or _____

because _____

_____

_____

Number of brave deeds I have done

_____

Please color the turkey. (It's a Grandma)

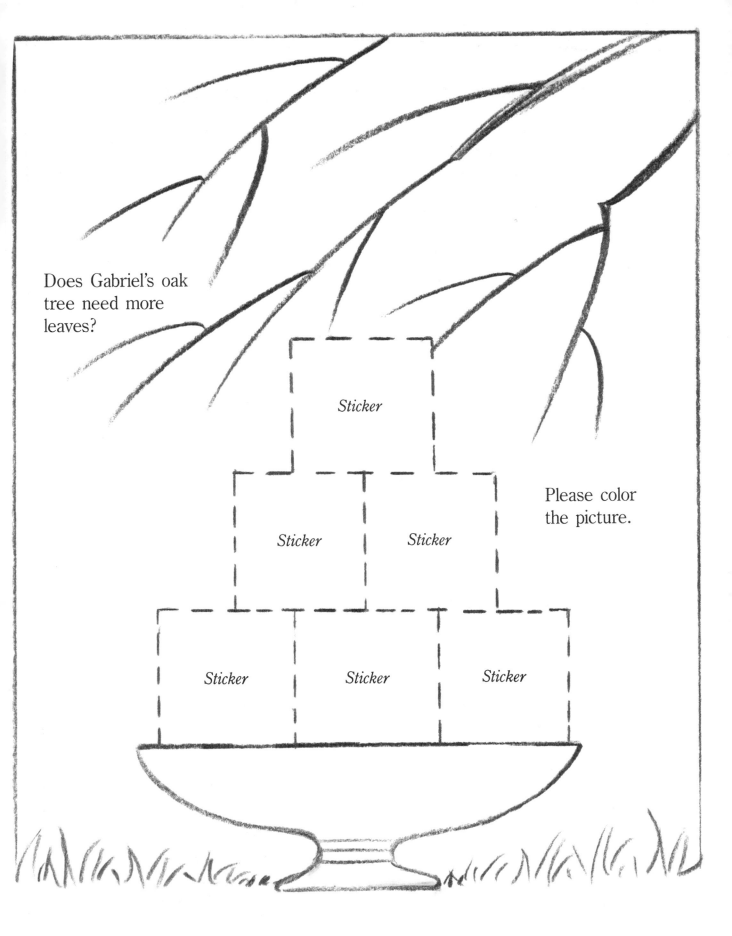

Does Gabriel's oak tree need more leaves?

Sticker

Sticker *Sticker*

Please color the picture.

Sticker *Sticker* *Sticker*

MAESTRO GROUNDHOG'S REWARD

Willa Weasel's Tips for Being Thankful

1. It is important to be thankful,
   because being unthankful is not nice.
   Also, being thankful makes you feel good.

2. The best way to be thankful
   is to give thanks every day for good things.
   Then you can feel good each day of the year,
   instead of on only one day.

3. Some people are not good at being thankful
   on Thanksgiving, because they have too many things
   to remember from all year long.
   By the time they have finished giving thanks
   for all of it, it's bedtime, and they do not have time
   to eat dinner.

4. So if you do not have too much to be thankful for on
   Thanksgiving Day, well oh my! You can be thankful
   for that, because you can be finished giving thanks
   in hardly any time at all.

5. Then you will have the rest of the day to enjoy
   your big dinner, and especially to enjoy
   all your family and friends who get together
   for Thanksgiving Day.

6. Remember — be thankful every day.
   Then when Thanksgiving comes, you can feel wonderful
   because you have been practicing thankfulness all year,
   and you are very good at it.

1. True or False or Maybe

On Thanksgiving Day, people should be thankful for all their relatives and friends.

Cousins are always very good friends, especially when they are the same age.

It is possible to have an Uncle or Aunt who is younger than you are.

Grown-up children come home for Thanksgiving because their parents can't eat a whole turkey by themselves.

If you are not good at saying grace for Thanksgiving dinner, it takes too long and the food gets cold.

Loving and being loved is the most important thing for which to be thankful.

2. After 500,000 years of backward evolution:

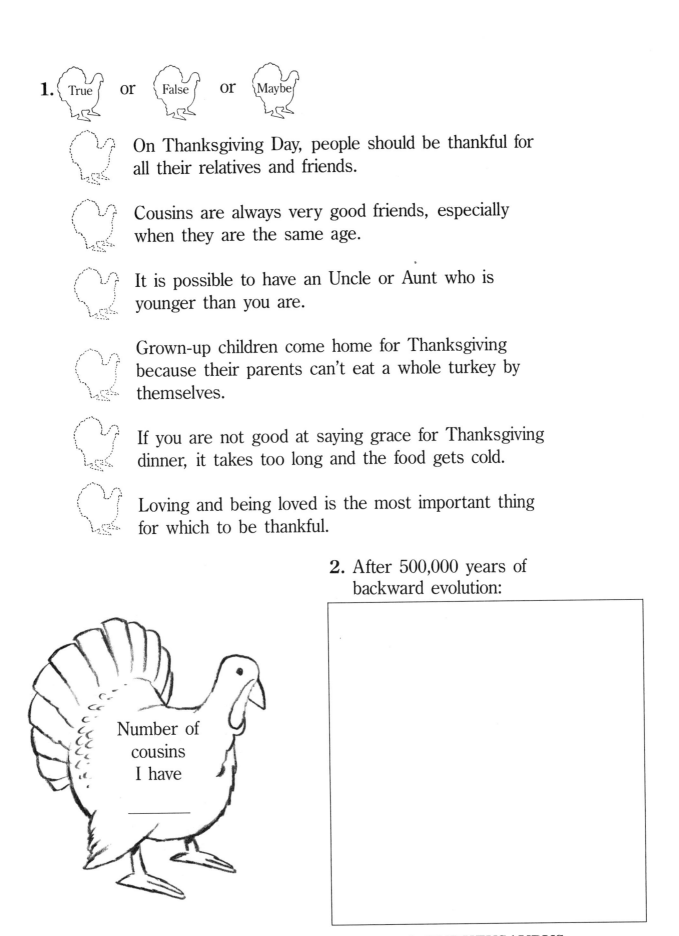

Number of cousins I have

_____

Please color the Grandpa.

A TURKEYSAURUS

THE OWL GOOPERS WISH TO ANNOUNCE THAT THE TURKEYS HAVE FOUND THEIR FREEDOM

The Owls have deduced that the turkeys left when they saw there was no patrol. They are not back at the farm, because the farmer is still looking for them. Therefore, they must have returned to the wild. Since they have learned to find their own food, they will be able to look after themselves.

THE OWL GOOPERS WISH TO THANK YOU FOR YOUR ATTENTION

1. The Owl Goopers' explanation
   about the turkeys is right.

   _____ Yes or _____ No, because

   _____

   _____

   _____

   _____

   _____

   _____

2. After 5,000,000 years of
   backward evolution:

   [ ]

   A Tyranno-Turkey

3. True or False or Maybe

   When the last dinosaurs
   died about 60 million years
   ago, it was reported in the
   Dinosaur Daily News.

   The word dinosaur comes from
   a Greek word which means
   "terrible lizard."

   If you don't mind bugs, you
   can have your own burrow
   in an autumn leaf pile.

   When four people each think
   the other one is doing a job,
   it gets done four times.

4. Raking leaves is:
   (circle your answers)

   fascinating

   clean work

   good exercise

   tedious

   _____

   Playing in the leaf pile is:

   delightful

   bouncy

   creepy

   _____

Walter Weasel's Instructions
For Celebrating Thanksgiving Day

1. Celebrate Thanksgiving with a Thank You Feast that is big enough.

2. A feast is big enough when you have food left over, because leftovers prove that you have more than you need.

3. Invite your family and friends to share your feast.

4. Before feasting, give thanks for:
   a. family and friends
   b. good health and good times
   c. having more than you need

5. If you are unable to provide such a feast, then make sure that you are still a Good Friend to your friends.

6. Have yourself invited, as a Good Friend, to a friend's feast.

7. Bring something besides yourself to this feast, such as food.

8. If you cannot bring food, then bring flowers, or branches of autumn leaves instead.

9. As you fall asleep on Thanksgiving night, think of something extra to be thankful for. If you cannot think of anything, choose from the following:
   a. that there are enough colors for a rainbow.
   b. that your hair grows out instead of in.
   c. that you speak a language you can understand.
   d. that coconuts fall down instead of up.

Sticker		Sticker		Sticker
Mums to bring	or	a giant dahlia	or	hibiscus flowers

1. 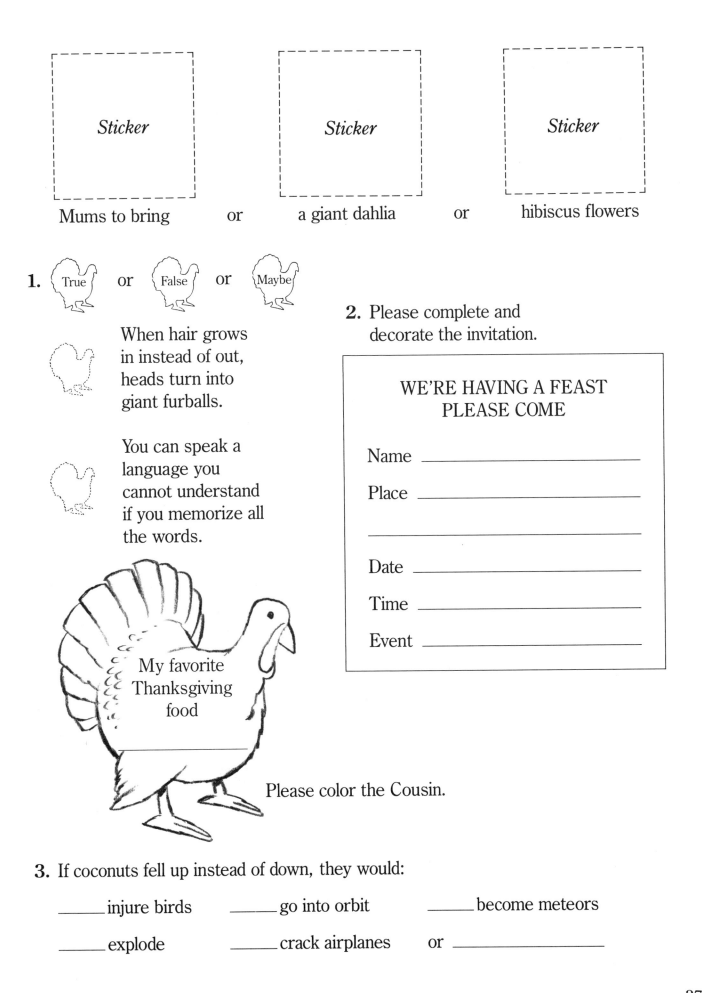 True or False or Maybe

When hair grows in instead of out, heads turn into giant furballs.

You can speak a language you cannot understand if you memorize all the words.

My favorite Thanksgiving food

Please color the Cousin.

2. Please complete and decorate the invitation.

WE'RE HAVING A FEAST
PLEASE COME

Name _____

Place _____

_____

Date _____

Time _____

Event _____

3. If coconuts fell up instead of down, they would:

_____ injure birds _____ go into orbit _____ become meteors

_____ explode _____ crack airplanes or _____

"A THOUSAND THANK YOUS TO GIVE"

Elvie L. Butler

I am thank-ful for my head, my ears, my eyes, I am thank-ful for my
As much as I need food and shoes and books, I need love that nev-er

legs, my toes, my feet; and if I were a bird, a love-ly
ends, that nev-er ends; and so when I give thanks for ev-'ry-

bird, I'd be thank-ful for my song, my wings, my beak. I have
thing, I am thank-ful for my friends, for all my friends. I have

ten times ten times ten, a thou-sand thank yous to give. Yes, I have

ten times ten times ten, a thou-sand thank yous to give.

Three Meadowlarks

Five Hummingbirds

Drummer Rabbit

Three Red Cardinals

Three Froghorn Frogs

One Crow

Two Harp Squirrels

┌──────────┐   ┌──────────┐   ┌──────────┐
│   │   │   │   │   │
│ *Sticker* │   │ *Sticker* │   │ *Sticker* │
│   │   │   │   │   │
└──────────┘   └──────────┘   └──────────┘
  Pumpkin Pie   Roast corn cob   Toasted marshmallow

1. The friends from the forest who stayed for Thanksgiving

Dinner probably brought: _____ chestnuts _____

cranberries _____ pizza _____ acorns _____ tortillas _____

bannock bread _____ chop suey _____ walnuts _____

corn fritters _____ fall leaves _____ flowers or _____

2. Please finish the news report.

┌─────────────────────────────┐
│   **THE GREENFIELD**   │
│   **GAZETTE**   │
│   │
│   * * * * * *   │
│   │
│ The Thanksgiving Concert in the │
│   │
│ Big Green Field was _____ │
│   │
│ _____ │
│   │
│ _____ │
│   │
│ _____ │
│   │
│ _____ │
│   │
│ _____ │
└─────────────────────────────┘

3. Please write your own
"Welcome to Thanksgiving."

Good-bye, _____

Hello, _____

Good-bye, _____

Hello, _____

Good-bye, _____

Hello, _____

_____

Dear Me,

It's Thanksgiving night, and I feel very happy. I also feel

_____ and _____.

For Thanksgiving decorations, we put up _____

and also some _____. For our Thanksgiving dinner,

we had _____ and _____, and

_____ and _____. (If you need

more space, use next page.)

This year we shared Thanksgiving with _____

and _____.

I wish we could have seen _____,

too, but they couldn't make it. Maybe we will see them at

Christmastime.

Now it's time to plan for Christmas, which is Willa Weasel's "very

most favorite time of year!"

For Christmas, I plan to make presents for _____

and _____. I will make a _____

and perhaps a _____. If I can earn enough

money, I shall buy some presents, too.

Now I shall finish Thanksgiving with Walter Weasel's last Instruction.

I'll snuggle up in my bed and think of something extra for which to be

thankful. It will probably be _____.

L O V E ,
M E

Please color the
brilliant oak leaf.

—— NOTES ——

More About Thanksgiving and Me

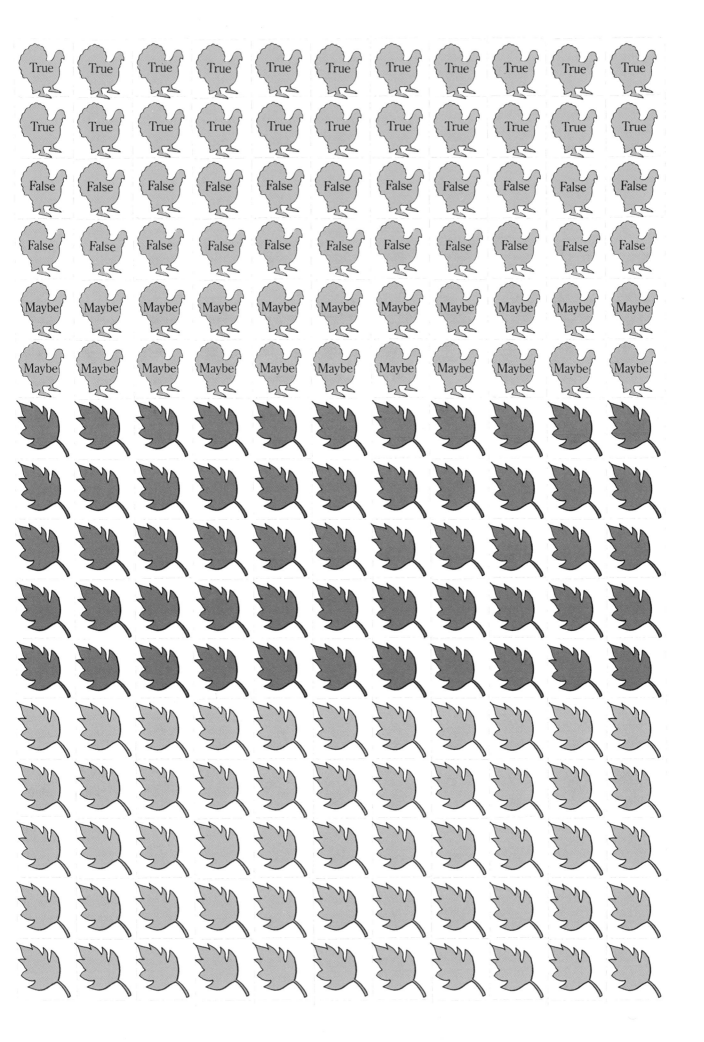